Specific Skill Series

Working Within Words

Richard A. Boning

Fifth Edition

SRA/McGraw-Hill
Columbus, Ohio

Cover, Back Cover, Ron Sanford/The Stock Market

SRA/McGraw-Hill

A Division of The McGraw·Hill Companies

Printed in the United States of America.

Send all inquiries to:
    SRA/McGraw-Hill
    8787 Orion Place
    Columbus, OH 43240-4027

ISBN 0-02-687923-9

7 8 IPC 02 01

PURPOSE:

WORKING WITHIN WORDS helps pupils put sounds and other word elements to work to determine word meaning. Many units in WORKING WITHIN WORDS develop understandings about sound-symbol (phonic) associations. Other units treat letter combinations, syllabication, roots and affixes, accent patterns, compound words, longer words, and spelling changes caused by adding endings.

FOR WHOM:

The skill of WORKING WITHIN WORDS is developed through a series of books spanning ten levels (Picture, Preparatory, A, B, C, D, E, F, G, H). The Picture Level is for pupils who have not acquired a basic sight vocabulary. The Preparatory Level is for pupils who have a basic sight vocabulary but are not yet ready for the first-grade-level book. Books A through H are appropriate for pupils who can read on levels one through eight, respectively. **The use of the *Specific Skill Series Placement Test* is recommended to determine the appropriate level.**

THE NEW EDITION:

The fifth edition of the *Specific Skill Series* maintains the quality and focus that has distinguished this program for more than 25 years. A key element central to the program's success has been the unique nature of the reading selections. Nonfiction pieces about current topics have been designed to stimulate the interest of students, motivating them to use the comprehension strategies they have learned to further their reading. To keep this important aspect of the program intact, a percentage of the reading selections have been replaced in order to ensure the continued relevance of the subject material.

In addition, a significant percentage of the artwork in the program has been replaced to give the books a contemporary look. The cover photographs are designed to appeal to readers of all ages.

SESSIONS:

Short practice sessions are the most effective. It is desirable to have a practice session every day or every other day, using a few units each session.

SCORING:

Pupils should record their answers on the reproducible worksheets. The worksheets make scoring easier and provide uniform records of the pupils' work. Using worksheets also avoids consuming the exercise books.

To the Teacher

It is important for pupils to know how well they are doing. For this reason, units should be scored as soon as they have been completed. Then a discussion can be held in which pupils justify their choices. (The Integrated Language Activities, many of which are open-ended, do not lend themselves to an objective score; thus there are no answer keys for these pages.)

GENERAL INFORMATION ON *WORKING WITHIN WORDS*:

The units are of two types: concept builders and functional exercises. The concept units focus the reader's attention on common patterns and parts of words. Each generalization is built step-by-step on the structure of previously formed concepts. The functional exercises either follow the concept units or are contained within them. They provide the reader with many immediate and repeated experiences with words involving particular patterns or principles. Sentence settings are typical for the pupils' level; often the choices offered are new words.

As WORKING WITHIN WORDS progresses through different word elements there is constant reinforcement. The more elementary booklets focus on phonic elements such as consonant sounds, consonant substitutions, blends, phonograms, and vowel sounds. As the level of difficulty increases, the emphasis shifts to syllabication, prefixes, suffixes, and roots.

A unit-by-unit list of concepts developed in this book is found on page 64.

INSTRUCTIONS:

Minimal direction is required. Pupils' attention must be drawn to the answer choices. In the concept units only two or three answer choices are offered. In the units that provide application of understandings, four to nine answer choices are offered, providing more experiences with words of a particular pattern. In units which offer an *F* choice, the *F* stands for NONE. This means that none of the choices makes sense in that particular setting.

RELATED MATERIALS:

Specific Skill Series Placement Tests, which enable the teacher to place pupils at their appropriate levels in each skill, are available for the Elementary (Pre-1–6) and Midway (4–8) grade levels.

About This Book

In written words, letters stand for sounds. A reader **decodes** a word the way a spy decodes a secret message. If you know the sounds that letters stand for, you can begin to unlock the secret message of a word.

Knowing the sounds of a word is only a beginning. Just as a secret message may have many parts, a word may have more than one part, too. In order to read and understand a word, you need to understand the parts of the word.

Words can be divided into **syllables**. A syllable is a word part that contains a **vowel sound**. The word *dog* has just one vowel sound. It is a one-syllable word. The word *rocket* has two vowel sounds. It is a two-syllable word. How many syllables does the word *syllable* have?

Word parts can be added to words to create new words with new meanings. For example, *joyful* means "full of joy." What do you think *hopeful* means?

In this book, you will study many words. You will learn to recognize the parts of words and patterns in words. Then you will use what you have learned. As you unlock the meanings of the words in this book, you will be practicing the skills of a master decoder!

1. All of the twenty-six _____ in the alphabet are consonants or vowels.

   (A) numbers   **(B) sentences**   **(C) letters**

2. The letters **a, e, i, o, u** (and sometimes **y**) are called vowels. There are _____ of them not counting **y**.

   (A) five   **(B) ten**   **(C) none**

3. The other letters are called _____.

   (A) consonants   **(B) colors**   **(C) sums**

4. Each of the vowels has a long and a short sound. When a vowel says its own name, it is said to have a long _____.

   (A) time   **(B) sound**   **(C) kind**

5. Look at the vowels in the words **go, hi, we.** The vowel is at the _____ of each word.

   (A) top   **(B) start**   **(C) end**

6. Say the words **go, hi, we.** The vowels have long _____.

   (A) sounds   **(B) numbers**   **(C) silent**

7. Look at the vowels in the words **run, cat, hop.** Each vowel is in the _____ of the word.

   (A) start   **(B) end**   **(C) middle**

8. Say the words **run, cat, hop.** The _____ have short sounds.

   (A) consonants   **(B) vowels**   **(C) numbers**

9. When there is one vowel and that vowel is in the middle of a word, it usually has a _____ sound.

   (A) silent   **(B) short**   **(C) long**

10. When there is one vowel and that vowel is at the end of the word, it usually has a _____ sound.

    (A) short   **(B) long**   **(C) nice**

UNIT 2
Building Vowel Concepts

1. The words **my, cry, sky** end with the letter **y**. The **y** at the end sounds like a long _____.

   (A) **u**   (B) **i**   (C) **o**

2. The words **happy, sunny, Betty** end with the letter **y**. The **y** at the end sounds like a long _____.

   (A) **r**   (B) **u**   (C) **e**

3. When the letter **y** has the sound of a vowel, it is called a vowel. When **y** does not have the sound of a vowel, it is called a _____.

   (A) **consonant**   (B) **name**   (C) **number**

4. To show that a vowel has a long sound, a _____ is put over it, as in the word **hīde.**

   (A) **number**   (B) **line**   (C) **word**

5. The marks over the words **bāke, kīnd, hōme** all show that the vowels have _____ sounds.

   (A) **long**   (B) **silent**   (C) **new**

6. To show that a vowel has a short _____, a curved line is put over it, as in the word **run.**

   (A) **haircut**   (B) **sound**   (C) **silent**

7. The marks over the vowels in the words **hăt, fŭn, dĭd, yĕs, gŏt** all show that the vowels are _____.

   (A) **long**   (B) **short**   (C) **small**

8. Look at the vowels in the words **at, in, egg, ox, up.** The vowels _____ these words.

   (A) **start**   (B) **end**   (C) **not**

9. Say the words **at, in, egg, ox, up.** The vowels have _____ sounds.

   (A) **short**   (B) **long**   (C) **new**

10. When a vowel comes at the start of a short word, the _____ usually has a short sound.

    (A) **vowel**   (B) **consonant**   (C) **numbers**

1. I started to _____ my fingers to the music.
   (A) rage   (B) ham   (C) plan
   (D) track   (E) snap   (F) NONE

2. Jan gave each person in her _____ a piece of fruit.
   (A) sand   (B) fact   (C) clam
   (D) class   (E) black   (F) NONE

3. If it gets too warm, you may turn on the _____.
   (A) crab   (B) wagon   (C) slap
   (D) past   (E) cap   (F) NONE

4. Don't _____ the food off the table.
   (A) gas   (B) flat   (C) grab
   (D) rag   (E) trap   (F) NONE

5. Rosa was proud to carry the _____ in the parade.
   (A) last   (B) flag   (C) flap
   (D) rat   (E) drank   (F) NONE

6. We _____ all the way across the river.
   (A) glad   (B) ask   (C) match
   (D) sad   (E) grass   (F) NONE

7. The _____ played many songs that I knew.
   (A) swam   (B) clap   (C) tan
   (D) drag   (E) band   (F) NONE

8. Juan and I will go to _____ this summer.
   (A) back   (B) lap   (C) camp
   (D) pan   (E) mat   (F) NONE

9. Hold his _____ when you cross the street.
   (A) map   (B) hand   (C) lamp
   (D) can   (E) mask   (F) NONE

10. Help me _____ when I go on the trip.
    (A) grand   (B) fact   (C) ham
    (D) gas   (E) pack   (F) NONE

UNIT 4
Short Vowel i Practice

1. Ron and Pat did not want to _____ the bus.
   - (A) grin
   - (B) limp
   - (C) still
   - (D) miss
   - (E) hill
   - (F) NONE

2. Ann learned to _____ when she was six years old.
   - (A) pill
   - (B) tin
   - (C) swim
   - (D) tick
   - (E) brick
   - (F) NONE

3. Juan watched the water as it _____ into the sink.
   - (A) fist
   - (B) snip
   - (C) grip
   - (D) it
   - (E) dig
   - (F) NONE

4. Sue quickly lifted the blue glass to her _____.
   - (A) sip
   - (B) trip
   - (C) spill
   - (D) drip
   - (E) shift
   - (F) NONE

5. Beth gave Mother a _____ before she went to work.
   - (A) skim
   - (B) bill
   - (C) did
   - (D) swift
   - (E) kiss
   - (F) NONE

6. It took a long time to climb the _____.
   - (A) risk
   - (B) silk
   - (C) mill
   - (D) kick
   - (E) hill
   - (F) NONE

7. She _____ behind the oak tree near the barn.
   - (A) list
   - (B) hint
   - (C) win
   - (D) hid
   - (E) six
   - (F) NONE

8. Jill can _____ much faster than she can walk.
   - (A) mist
   - (B) bring
   - (C) fill
   - (D) clip
   - (E) skip
   - (F) NONE

9. Andy ran to the door when he heard the bell _____.
   - (A) swing
   - (B) drip
   - (C) spin
   - (D) ring
   - (E) chick
   - (F) NONE

10. They saw a _____ and cow at the farm.
    - (A) blink
    - (B) click
    - (C) slip
    - (D) pick
    - (E) pig
    - (F) NONE

1. Mother was able to open the _____ with her key.

   (A) spot   (B) trot   (C) bomb

   (D) lock   (E) rock   (F) NONE

2. All cars must _____ when the light turns red.

   (A) drop   (B) dot   (C) dock

   (D) top   (E) pop   (F) NONE

3. We bought Sam a toy _____ for his birthday.

   (A) rob   (B) hop   (C) hot

   (D) not   (E) got   (F) NONE

4. A _____ is known to be a very clever animal.

   (A) doll   (B) flock   (C) mob

   (D) pot   (E) fox   (F) NONE

5. Ann asked if she could sail her boat on the _____.

   (A) block   (B) clock   (C) pond

   (D) cot   (E) plop   (F) NONE

6. Place the _____ on the stove.

   (A) mop   (B) pot   (C) slot

   (D) nod   (E) stop   (F) NONE

7. Let us go into the _____ next door.

   (A) hog   (B) rod   (C) drop

   (D) shop   (E) pot   (F) NONE

8. The _____ of corn was ready to be gathered.

   (A) Bob   (B) sock   (C) cop

   (D) crop   (E) nod   (F) NONE

9. We will use an ax to _____ the wood.

   (A) Tom   (B) chop   (C) spot

   (D) knock   (E) lock   (F) NONE

10. I slept on a _____ in the tent.

    (A) pop   (B) mop   (C) block

    (D) cot   (E) chop   (F) NONE

1. We gave our dog a bath in a _____.

   (A) dust   (B) jump   (C) gun
   (D) rug   (E) tub   (F) NONE

2. The children saw a _____ in the middle of the pond.

   (A) must   (B) fun   (C) grunt
   (D) stuck   (E) dug   (F) NONE

3. Father asked John what all the _____ was about.

   (A) luck   (B) sun   (C) fuss
   (D) dump   (E) lump   (F) NONE

4. We often _____ a song when we don't know the words.

   (A) hut   (B) hung   (C) spun
   (D) hum   (E) rust   (F) NONE

5. I filled the _____ with milk from the large bottle.

   (A) cut   (B) puff   (C) cup
   (D) rub   (E) run   (F) NONE

6. Rosa _____ her hand into the cold water.

   (A) mud   (B) tub   (C) hug
   (D) drum   (E) pup   (F) NONE

7. How many people can ride in the _____?

   (A) shut   (B) bus   (C) up
   (D) nut   (E) gum   (F) NONE

8. The water was filled with _____ from all the soap.

   (A) bump   (B) buns   (C) plugs
   (D) pump   (E) suds   (F) NONE

9. Jan did not like to eat the _____ of the bread.

   (A) rush   (B) stunt   (C) cub
   (D) hung   (E) sudden   (F) NONE

10. How many legs are on the _____?

    (A) tug   (B) gun   (C) supper
    (D) bug   (E) truck   (F) NONE

1. One of the eggs fell from the _____.

   (A) held   (B) let   (C) nest

   (D) step   (E) blend   (F) NONE

2. Rosa and Juan stood on the _____ of the ship.

   (A) dent   (B) spend   (C) stem

   (D) deck   (E) sled   (F) NONE

3. Chickens like to _____ when they are being fed.

   (A) pest   (B) spell   (C) best

   (D) sled   (E) net   (F) NONE

4. Can all of us sit on the _____?

   (A) lamp   (B) bench   (C) rent

   (D) slept   (E) tend   (F) NONE

5. Mother and Ron _____ to the store to buy clothes.

   (A) bent   (B) met   (C) tent

   (D) best   (E) press   (F) NONE

6. When the sun came out, the snow began to _____.

   (A) bet   (B) belt   (C) mend

   (D) less   (E) melt   (F) NONE

7. Joan and I did not like _____.

   (A) well   (B) bend   (C) end

   (D) check   (E) test   (F) NONE

8. The sun goes down in the _____ every evening.

   (A) nest   (B) mess   (C) yet

   (D) dress   (E) west   (F) NONE

9. Tom told Jan not to _____ the others his secret.

   (A) bell   (B) men   (C) shell

   (D) hen   (E) tell   (F) NONE

10. Kate is able to write very well with a _____.

    (A) spend   (B) help   (C) leg

    (D) peck   (E) pen   (F) NONE

1. The _____ jumped across the pond.
(A) patch	(B) step	(C) frog
(D) shell	(E) clap	(F) NONE

2. Frank said that he would take out the _____.
(A) flash	(B) dash	(C) crisp
(D) trip	(E) trash	(F) NONE

3. We put the tools in a _____ behind the house.
(A) shut	(B) sting	(C) smash
(D) crush	(E) crust	(F) NONE

4. Beth ate the _____ of grapes she had picked.
(A) brush	(B) chick	(C) stamp
(D) bunch	(E) dress	(F) NONE

5. Father told Sam to buy bread that was _____.
(A) desk	(B) trick	(C) fish
(D) fresh	(E) plant	(F) NONE

6. Steve went upstairs to _____ his teeth.
(A) dish	(B) brush	(C) clam
(D) much	(E) twin	(F) NONE

7. Karen took the _____ out of her pocketbook.
(A) ranch	(B) shelf	(C) tent
(D) slam	(E) chin	(F) NONE

8. Did you see Barbara _____ the ball?
(A) catch	(B) flat	(C) stunt
(D) bunch	(E) hatch	(F) NONE

9. Mark found a _____ in the sand at the beach.
(A) bring	(B) hush	(C) grin
(D) mash	(E) slam	(F) NONE

10. Ann helped Bob _____ the wood for the fire.
(A) spit	(B) think	(C) shot
(D) chop	(E) lamp	(F) NONE

1. Say the words **bake, rope, time, use.** Each of these words ends with a silent **e.** The vowel before the _____ says its own name.

    (A) e   **(B) x**   **(C) v**

2. Words that end with the silent **e** are also often called **Magic e** words because the **e** makes the _____ before it say its own name.

    (A) vowel   **(B) consonant**   **(C) word**

3. Say the word **hop.** Add an **e** to the end and it becomes **hope.** The _____ now says its own name. The word **hope** rhymes with **rope.**

    (A) n   **(B) o**   **(C) e**

4. Say the word **hat.** Add an **e** to the end and it becomes **hate.** The _____ now says its own name. The word **hate** rhymes with **late.**

    (A) a   **(B) e**   **(C) p**

5. Say the word **ripe.** Take away the **e** at the end and it becomes **rip.** Without the **Magic e** the vowel **i** gives a _____ sound. The word rhymes with **lip.**

    (A) silent   **(B) short**   **(C) white**

6. Say the word **cute.** Take away the **e** at the end and it becomes **cut.** Without the **Magic e** the vowel _____ gives a short sound. The word rhymes with **but.**

    (A) r   **(B) i**   **(C) u**

7. Look at the words **make** and **making.** The **e** at the end of the word **make** is dropped before the ending **ing** is _____ .

    (A) added   **(B) cut**   **(C) found**

8. Look at the words **ride** and **riding.** The **e** at the end of the word **ride** is dropped before the ending _____ is added.

    (A) ing   **(B) t**   **(C) ish**

9. Say the words **make** and **making.** The vowel **a** says its own name in the word **make.** It also says its own _____ in the word **making.**

    (A) short   **(B) silent**   **(C) name**

10. Say the words **taking, biting, roping, using.** In each of these words the first vowel says its own name just as it does before the **Magic e** is _____ .

    (A) short   **(B) dropped**   **(C) liked**

1. The sun did not _____ today.
   - (A) time
   - (B) while
   - (C) plane
   - (D) shine
   - (E) ride
   - (F) NONE

2. Juan's little brother is in the second _____.
   - (A) shape
   - (B) spike
   - (C) grape
   - (D) smile
   - (E) grade
   - (F) NONE

3. Would you like to _____ your mother's car?
   - (A) bride
   - (B) slave
   - (C) place
   - (D) drive
   - (E) tribe
   - (F) NONE

4. Linda said she is going to buy a new _____.
   - (A) price
   - (B) whine
   - (C) fine
   - (D) stale
   - (E) blaze
   - (F) NONE

5. Who will win the _____?
   - (A) trace
   - (B) shame
   - (C) poke
   - (D) hide
   - (E) prize
   - (F) NONE

6. Tom walked to the top of the _____.
   - (A) five
   - (B) flame
   - (C) face
   - (D) froze
   - (E) chose
   - (F) NONE

7. Please _____ when I take your picture.
   - (A) same
   - (B) trade
   - (C) smile
   - (D) flake
   - (E) mile
   - (F) NONE

8. Sam had a large _____ of paper on his desk.
   - (A) line
   - (B) pile
   - (C) blade
   - (D) same
   - (E) ride
   - (F) NONE

9. I'm sorry I _____ your bike.
   - (A) whale
   - (B) twice
   - (C) broke
   - (D) stage
   - (E) cute
   - (F) NONE

10. Lisa gave each person a _____ of cake.
    - (A) glide
    - (B) pole
    - (C) these
    - (D) skate
    - (E) slice
    - (F) NONE

1. Say the words **goat, seat, rain, sleep.** In each of these words there are two
   _____.

   (A) r's   (B) vowels   (C) o's

2. In each of the words **goat, seat, rain, sleep** the _____ vowels are together.
   (A) ten   (B) two   (C) one

3. The words **goat, seat, rain, sleep** are called **Double Vowel** words _____
   they have two vowels together.
   (A) consonants   (B) not   (C) because

4. In the word **goat** we see the vowels **oa.** The **o** says its own name and the
   _____ is silent.
   (A) t   (B) a   (C) b

5. In the word **seat** we see the vowels **ea.** The **e** says its own name and the
   _____ vowel is silent.
   (A) other   (B) third   (C) number

6. In the word **rain** we see the vowels **ai.** The _____ says its own name and
   the next vowel is silent.
   (A) a   (B) i   (C) o

7. In the word **sleep** we see the vowels **ee.** The first **e** says its own _____ and
   the second **e** is silent.
   (A) address   (B) name   (C) age

8. In most words having an **oa, ea, ai, ee,** the first _____ says its own name
   and the second vowel is silent.
   (A) consonant   (B) vowel   (C) number

9. There are some _____, however, in which the first vowel is not long, even
   though there are two vowels together.
   (A) stories   (B) pictures   (C) words

10. Say the words **bread** and **head.** Even though each of these words has two
    vowels together, the first vowel is not _____.
    (A) long   (B) bought   (C) silent

16

UNIT 12
Double Vowel Practice

1. I could not _____ the can on the shelf.
   - (A) beach
   - (B) beat
   - (C) reach
   - (D) least
   - (E) rain
   - (F) NONE

2. Sam says he tries to do a good _____ every day.
   - (A) feast
   - (B) steam
   - (C) float
   - (D) team
   - (E) main
   - (F) NONE

3. Please _____ in the hall.
   - (A) boat
   - (B) plain
   - (C) brain
   - (D) drain
   - (E) wait
   - (F) NONE

4. The large ship will _____ across the ocean.
   - (A) speak
   - (B) sail
   - (C) bleed
   - (D) dried
   - (E) grain
   - (F) NONE

5. The big dump truck was loaded with _____.
   - (A) neat
   - (B) need
   - (C) heat
   - (D) speed
   - (E) steep
   - (F) NONE

6. Mother said that we will not _____ if we study.
   - (A) meat
   - (B) waist
   - (C) fail
   - (D) claim
   - (E) weak
   - (F) NONE

7. Who baked the _____ of bread?
   - (A) loaf
   - (B) steal
   - (C) beam
   - (D) steer
   - (E) roast
   - (F) NONE

8. Dan went to the door to see if we had any _____.
   - (A) groan
   - (B) deep
   - (C) mail
   - (D) hear
   - (E) real
   - (F) NONE

9. Kelly could not get her boat to _____.
   - (A) deal
   - (B) seat
   - (C) foam
   - (D) tail
   - (E) bead
   - (F) NONE

10. I saw water _____ from the pipe.
    - (A) load
    - (B) moan
    - (C) paint
    - (D) leak
    - (E) week
    - (F) NONE

A. Exercising Your Skill

Draw a line down the middle of your paper. Label the sides **net** and **neat**.

net	neat

Read the words below. Listen to the vowel sound in each one. Does it sound like **net** or like **neat**? On your paper, write each word under the word with the same vowel sound.

1.	feet	2.	sent	3.	rest
4.	beast	5.	deck	6.	spent
7.	weak	8.	held	9.	wheel
10.	fetch	11.	creek	12.	treat

B. Expanding Your Skill

Read the words in the box. Copy all the words that have a **long** vowel sound.

hog	whale	toad
crane	bug	sheep
crab	seal	fly
snail	mole	ant

Compare your paper with that of a classmate. If you have different answers, look up the words in a dictionary to find the correct vowel sounds.

C. Exploring Language

Read each sentence. Look at the word with a line under it. That word has the wrong vowel sound. What word should it be? For each underlined word, write a word on your paper that makes sense. Do this by changing, dropping, or adding one or more vowels.

1. We watched the <u>beets</u> sailing on the lake.
2. Carrie had a string of <u>beds</u> around her neck.
3. The tall <u>mane</u> walked into the house.
4. We planted a <u>pin</u> tree in the yard.
5. Bill had to <u>tag</u> hard before the heavy wagon would move.
6. Sal was afraid of the old billy <u>got</u> at the farm.
7. We picked apples from the <u>try</u>.
8. There were three fat <u>pegs</u> in the pen.

D. Expressing Yourself

Choose one of these things.

1. Make up a sentence for each vowel (**a**, **e**, **i**, **o**, and **u**). Use both the short vowel sound and the long vowel sound in the sentence. See how many times you can use each. Here is a sample, for long **a** and short **a**.

   The <u>rain</u> <u>ran</u> down the <u>drain</u>.

2. Go to the library. Find fun facts about animals. Tell each fact to the class. Give clues about the sounds in the animal's name. See if your classmates can guess what animal matches each fact.

   Here is an example:

   "This tiny animal can jump 300 times its own length. It has a long vowel sound in its name. The first two letters are **fl**. What is it?" [a flea]

1. The leg is broken on this _____.
    (A) brake   (B) plane   (C) glide
    (D) clean   (E) chair   (F) NONE

2. I spread butter and jam on the _____.
    (A) leap   (B) same   (C) spoke
    (D) toast   (E) steep   (F) NONE

3. We went for a _____ in the country.
    (A) smile   (B) hike   (C) grade
    (D) clean   (E) stair   (F) NONE

4. Can you _____ two languages?
    (A) speak   (B) shake   (C) like
    (D) strike   (E) beast   (F) NONE

5. Andy said that he was to _____ for the broken dish.
    (A) cheer   (B) mail   (C) east
    (D) seed   (E) cheap   (F) NONE

6. We need a new _____ in the kitchen.
    (A) stove   (B) least   (C) paint
    (D) trail   (E) gray   (F) NONE

7. How much _____ should I pour on the cereal?
    (A) float   (B) brain   (C) cream
    (D) dream   (E) neat   (F) NONE

8. Juan cleaned his _____ after each meal.
    (A) seem   (B) free   (C) while
    (D) teeth   (E) steam   (F) NONE

9. Kate said that she would like to _____ school.
    (A) train   (B) rise   (C) tribe
    (D) deal   (E) chain   (F) NONE

10. I saw a _____ puppy in the pet store.
    (A) sleep   (B) coat   (C) paint
    (D) shine   (E) cute   (F) NONE

UNIT 14
Consonant Blends and Digraphs

1. How did you **br**_____ the window?
   - **(A) ink**
   - **(B) ick**
   - **(C) eak**
   - **(D) ead**
   - **(E) oom**
   - **(F) NONE**

2. Tom **sp**_____ all his money before the day was over.
   - **(A) eed**
   - **(B) ace**
   - **(C) ill**
   - **(D) ent**
   - **(E) ell**
   - **(F) NONE**

3. Carry the drinks into the room on a **tr**_____.
   - **(A) ibe**
   - **(B) ade**
   - **(C) ay**
   - **(D) amp**
   - **(E) ick**
   - **(F) NONE**

4. Please **st**_____ carefully on the ice.
   - **(A) ain**
   - **(B) air**
   - **(C) ing**
   - **(D) ep**
   - **(E) ack**
   - **(F) NONE**

5. Beth and her **tw**_____ sister look just alike.
   - **(A) ig**
   - **(B) ice**
   - **(C) ist**
   - **(D) in**
   - **(E) elve**
   - **(F) NONE**

6. We feel **pr**_____ when we give the right answer.
   - **(A) ice**
   - **(B) int**
   - **(C) oof**
   - **(D) oud**
   - **(E) ess**
   - **(F) NONE**

7. What would you like to **dr**_____ with your meal?
   - **(A) aw**
   - **(B) ess**
   - **(C) ift**
   - **(D) op**
   - **(E) ink**
   - **(F) NONE**

8. Sandy asked Bill to pass the **cr**_____.
   - **(A) azy**
   - **(B) eam**
   - **(C) eep**
   - **(D) awl**
   - **(E) ied**
   - **(F) NONE**

9. Linda could see the **wh** _____ begin to turn.
   - **(A) ile**
   - **(B) eel**
   - **(C) en**
   - **(D) ich**
   - **(E) ite**
   - **(F) NONE**

10. Most growing plants are **gr**_____ in color.
    - **(A) ab**
    - **(B) unt**
    - **(C) oup**
    - **(D) ow**
    - **(E) ade**
    - **(F) NONE**

1. The sky grew dark and it began to **sn**_____.

   (A) ap   (B) ake   (C) iff
   (D) eeze   (E) ow   (F) NONE

2. Juan and I asked Pat to join the **cl**_____.

   (A) ear   (B) ean   (C) oud
   (D) ash   (E) ub   (F) NONE

3. Can you fix the broken plate with **gl**_____?

   (A) ow   (B) ad   (C) ide
   (D) ue   (E) ance   (F) NONE

4. We began to **cl**_____ when the team came on the field.

   (A) ose   (B) ub   (C) ap
   (D) oth   (E) ean   (F) NONE

5. A large **cr**_____ of people saw the circus parade.

   (A) ab   (B) ate   (C) ust
   (D) op   (E) oss   (F) NONE

6. Bob helped his mother **pl**_____ seeds in the garden.

   (A) ay   (B) ant   (C) um
   (D) ate   (E) ease   (F) NONE

7. We read my favorite **st**_____ in class.

   (A) ing   (B) ory   (C) ep
   (D) ick   (E) and   (F) NONE

8. The **br**_____ broke off from the tree.

   (A) ight   (B) eak   (C) anch
   (D) ave   (E) own   (F) NONE

9. The dog began to **ch**_____ the rabbit across the field.

   (A) in   (B) est   (C) op
   (D) eer   (E) ange   (F) NONE

10. I wanted to **sl**_____ at least eight hours.

    (A) eep   (B) ight   (C) ip
    (D) ow   (E) am   (F) NONE

1. Ron got a new **sl**_____ for a birthday present.

   (A) ap   (B) eep   (C) ip

   (D) ant   (E) ed   (F) NONE

2. Watch out or you will **sp**_____ the milk.

   (A) eed   (B) ill   (C) ank

   (D) oke   (E) in   (F) NONE

3. Watch me **gl**_____ on the ice.

   (A) ide   (B) ue   (C) ow

   (D) ance   (E) ad   (F) NONE

4. It is not easy to **ch**_____ down a large tree.

   (A) est   (B) eer   (C) ase

   (D) air   (E) ange   (F) NONE

5. The little rabbit made **tr**_____ in the snow.

   (A) ains   (B) eats   (C) ucks

   (D) ees   (E) acks   (F) NONE

6. Andy should **br**_____ his hair.

   (A) oken   (B) ush   (C) ing

   (D) idge   (E) ight   (F) NONE

7. The girls began to **sh**_____ as their team went ahead.

   (A) arp   (B) ell   (C) ark

   (D) eep   (E) out   (F) NONE

8. Maria could see the **sm**_____ coming from the building.

   (A) ile   (B) oke   (C) ack

   (D) ash   (E) all   (F) NONE

9. We always **cr**_____ the street at the corner.

   (A) ust   (B) ib   (C) ab

   (D) ack   (E) ush   (F) NONE

10. We had to **dr**_____ five miles to reach the park.

    (A) ill   (B) ink   (C) aw

    (D) ess   (E) um   (F) NONE

1. I must **th**_____ awhile before I answer.
   (A) ank   (B) ing   (C) ink
   (D) ick   (E) in   (F) NONE

2. Can't you stand **st**_____ for a moment?
   (A) art   (B) age   (C) eel
   (D) ill   (E) em   (F) NONE

3. A **sn**_____ has no legs but it can still move quickly.
   (A) ap   (B) ow   (C) ore
   (D) iff   (E) ake   (F) NONE

4. As the storm came near the wind began to **bl**_____.
   (A) eed   (B) ock   (C) ack
   (D) ame   (E) ue   (F) NONE

5. In cold weather there is **fr**_____ on the windows.
   (A) esh   (B) ee   (C) ame
   (D) ost   (E) ied   (F) NONE

6. There is not a **tr**_____ of dirt on the table.
   (A) ace   (B) ap   (C) ade
   (D) ick   (E) ay   (F) NONE

7. The painting is in a beautiful **fr**_____.
   (A) ost   (B) ee   (C) esh
   (D) ight   (E) og   (F) NONE

8. After the spring rain the flowers began to **bl**_____.
   (A) ock   (B) ack   (C) end
   (D) oom   (E) ame   (F) NONE

9. Ann had the highest spelling **sc**_____ in our class.
   (A) old   (B) ore   (C) out
   (D) ale   (E) ab   (F) NONE

10. Is there **sp**_____ for one more desk?
    (A) ice   (B) eak   (C) ace
    (D) oke   (E) it   (F) NONE

1. I am trying to draw a _____ line.

   (A) three   (B) screech   (C) straight
   (D) splash   (E) stretch   (F) NONE

2. Ron and Sue will _____ the kitchen floor for the party.

   (A) scrub   (B) shrub   (C) spread
   (D) scream   (E) throb   (F) NONE

3. Mother didn't want Juan to go out with a sore _____.

   (A) scrap   (B) strike   (C) scramble
   (D) throat   (E) thread   (F) NONE

4. A skunk has a white _____ running down its back.

   (A) through   (B) spring   (C) squeal
   (D) splint   (E) stripe   (F) NONE

5. Pat says she can _____ a ball high in the air.

   (A) scrape   (B) throw   (C) stray
   (D) sprout   (E) squeak   (F) NONE

6. Linda pulled a fish from the _____ near her home.

   (A) stream   (B) strung   (C) stroke
   (D) strong   (E) splinter   (F) NONE

7. Father asked Lisa to _____ water on the flowers.

   (A) strand   (B) sprinkle   (C) squad
   (D) scratch   (E) strip   (F) NONE

8. The children should not play in the _____.

   (A) street   (B) strap   (C) squint
   (D) screech   (E) shrink   (F) NONE

9. I will cut the _____ on the package.

   (A) square   (B) split   (C) string
   (D) throne   (E) streak   (F) NONE

10. The door does not _____ when I open it.

    (A) scream   (B) thrill   (C) sprang
    (D) streak   (E) strength   (F) NONE

1. There is no handle on this **c_____p.**
    (A) long i   (B) long u   (C) short u
    (D) short i   (E) short a   (F) NONE

2. Mother asked me to **cl_____se** the windows in the house.
    (A) long u   (B) short u   (C) long i
    (D) long o   (E) long e   (F) NONE

3. Lisa Simon got a new **d_____sk** for her room.
    (A) short a   (B) long a   (C) short i
    (D) long i   (E) long u   (F) NONE

4. Juan Rivera had fun playing with his new **k_____te.**
    (A) short i   (B) long i   (C) long u
    (D) short u   (E) short e   (F) NONE

5. My Uncle Jack often wears a large, black **h_____t.**
    (A) short i   (B) long i   (C) long o
    (D) short o   (E) short a   (F) NONE

6. Most people like to hear good **m_____sic** on the radio.
    (A) short o   (B) long o   (C) short i
    (D) long i   (E) long u   (F) NONE

7. It was difficult to walk up the **h_____ll.**
    (A) long a   (B) short e   (C) long i
    (D) short i   (E) long o   (F) NONE

8. We **w_____ve** good-by to a person who is leaving.
    (A) long i   (B) short i   (C) long o
    (D) long a   (E) short a   (F) NONE

9. The number between four and six is **f_____ve.**
    (A) long e   (B) short o   (C) long o
    (D) short i   (E) long i   (F) NONE

10. Please **g_____t** me a pencil and a piece of paper.
    (A) long a   (B) short e   (C) short i
    (D) long e   (E) long o   (F) NONE

1. I picked a red **r**_____**se** from the garden.
    - **(A) long e**
    - **(B) long o**
    - **(C) short i**
    - **(D) short e**
    - **(E) short o**
    - **(F) NONE**

2. Larry tried to **h**_____**t** the ball with his bat.
    - **(A) long a**
    - **(B) short a**
    - **(C) long e**
    - **(D) long u**
    - **(E) short o**
    - **(F) NONE**

3. Boys and girls like to ride on a **p**_____**ny.**
    - **(A) long a**
    - **(B) long i**
    - **(C) long o**
    - **(D) long u**
    - **(E) short i**
    - **(F) NONE**

4. Can you lift that heavy **r**_____**ck?**
    - **(A) long i**
    - **(B) short i**
    - **(C) long e**
    - **(D) long a**
    - **(E) short o**
    - **(F) NONE**

5. Jenny drew a dark **l**_____**ne** on the yellow paper.
    - **(A) short i**
    - **(B) long o**
    - **(C) short o**
    - **(D) long e**
    - **(E) long i**
    - **(F) NONE**

6. Some people like to eat **b**_____**con** with their eggs.
    - **(A) long u**
    - **(B) long o**
    - **(C) long i**
    - **(D) long a**
    - **(E) long e**
    - **(F) NONE**

7. We cannot keep a **s**_____**cret** if we give it away.
    - **(A) short a**
    - **(B) long a**
    - **(C) short e**
    - **(D) long e**
    - **(E) long o**
    - **(F) NONE**

8. In some games that we play we must **h**_____**p** on one leg.
    - **(A) short i**
    - **(B) long i**
    - **(C) long o**
    - **(D) short o**
    - **(E) long e**
    - **(F) NONE**

9. John smelled **sm**_____**ke** long before he saw the fire.
    - **(A) long a**
    - **(B) long e**
    - **(C) long o**
    - **(D) short i**
    - **(E) long u**
    - **(F) NONE**

10. Mother **pl**_____**ns** to go to the city on the train.
    - **(A) long i**
    - **(B) short i**
    - **(C) long e**
    - **(D) short a**
    - **(E) short u**
    - **(F) NONE**

1. In the summer, trees **sh_____de** us from the sun.
   - (A) long i
   - (B) long e
   - (C) long o
   - (D) long a
   - (E) long u
   - (F) NONE

2. A tall green **v_____ne** grew up the side of our house.
   - (A) long a
   - (B) short a
   - (C) long i
   - (D) long u
   - (E) long o
   - (F) NONE

3. Most children like to beat on a **dr_____m.**
   - (A) short e
   - (B) long u
   - (C) long a
   - (D) short i
   - (E) long o
   - (F) NONE

4. Pete wore a brown scarf around his **n_____ck.**
   - (A) short i
   - (B) long a
   - (C) long o
   - (D) short e
   - (E) short u
   - (F) NONE

5. Please put the food in this **b_____g.**
   - (A) long u
   - (B) short u
   - (C) long o
   - (D) long i
   - (E) short a
   - (F) NONE

6. Rosa went to the playground to play on the **sw_____ng.**
   - (A) long e
   - (B) short e
   - (C) long a
   - (D) short a
   - (E) long o
   - (F) NONE

7. Is it **_____asy** to add those numbers?
   - (A) long e
   - (B) short i
   - (C) short e
   - (D) long i
   - (E) short o
   - (F) NONE

8. We plan to **t_____ke** a long ride in the car.
   - (A) long e
   - (B) long o
   - (C) long a
   - (D) short u
   - (E) short a
   - (F) NONE

9. This is a **s_____fe** place to hide my money.
   - (A) long u
   - (B) long a
   - (C) short a
   - (D) long i
   - (E) short i
   - (F) NONE

10. My jacket was **w_____t** from the rain.
    - (A) short o
    - (B) short e
    - (C) long u
    - (D) long u
    - (E) long i
    - (F) NONE

1. The letters **ou** and **ow** make the same sound. The **ou** in the word **out** sounds like the _____ in the word **now**.

   (A) ow   (B) c   (C) t

2. The cat ran after the _____.

   (A) scout   (B) brown   (C) mouse
   (D) growl   (E) pound   (F) NONE

3. Farmers often use machines to _____ their fields.

   (A) thousand   (B) house   (C) hour
   (D) drown   (E) plow   (F) NONE

4. There are many beautiful _____ growing in the yard.

   (A) sour   (B) flowers   (C) crowd
   (D) found   (E) count   (F) NONE

5. In every word there is at least one _____.

   (A) vowel   (B) south   (C) ground
   (D) fowl   (E) proud   (F) NONE

6. The dog began to _____ when Bill went past.

   (A) cloud   (B) howl   (C) loud
   (D) allow   (E) sound   (F) NONE

7. The letters **oi** and **oy** make the same sound. The **oi** in the word **oil** sounds like the _____ in the word **boy**.

   (A) b   (B) oy   (C) r

8. Ron found a bright new _____ on the ground.

   (A) coin   (B) soil   (C) moist
   (D) noise   (E) joy   (F) NONE

9. The teacher asked Paul Sills to _____ our team.

   (A) join   (B) spoil   (C) Roy
   (D) toy   (E) point   (F) poison

10. The birds outside my window were _____.

    (A) boil   (B) joint   (C) royal
    (D) boys   (E) noisy   (F) NONE

1. The letters **aw** and **au** often make the same sound. The **aw** in the word **saw** sounds like _____ in the word **caught**.

    (A) gh   (B) t   (C) au

2. At _____ most people are still sound asleep.

    (A) paw   (B) dawn   (C) draw
    (D) August   (E) haul   (F) NONE

3. Can the bug _____ up that tree?

    (A) crawl   (B) claws   (C) yawn
    (D) awful   (E) lawn   (F) NONE

4. The leaves are very pretty during the _____.

    (A) daughter   (B) autumn   (C) hawk
    (D) awnings   (E) caught   (F) NONE

5. I _____ my brother how to swim this summer.

    (A) taught   (B) straw   (C) Paul
    (D) jaw   (E) saw   (F) NONE

6. The letters **ew** and **oo** often make the same sound. The **ew** in the word **new** sounds almost like the _____ in the word **soon**.

    (A) oo   (B) n   (C) s

7. I will need a _____ to sweep the floor.

    (A) blew   (B) spoon   (C) choose
    (D) crew   (E) broom   (F) NONE

8. We saw the airplane _____ down over the house.

    (A) zoom   (B) stew   (C) pool
    (D) booth   (E) smooth   (F) NONE

9. This hammer is a good _____.

    (A) toot   (B) stew   (C) tool
    (D) grew   (E) pool   (F) NONE

10. We _____ that we had to save money.

    (A) drew   (B) threw   (C) goose
    (D) troop   (E) flew   (F) NONE

1. Use a _____ knife to cut the apple.
   (A) smart   (B) March   (C) sharp
   (D) card   (E) barber   (F) NONE

2. He bought his new suit at that _____.
   (A) corn   (B) horn   (C) more
   (D) store   (E) north   (F) NONE

3. Will you _____ me for breaking the toy?
   (A) wore   (B) forgive   (C) forty
   (D) short   (E) shore   (F) NONE

4. We have a slide and a swing in our _____.
   (A) dark   (B) hard   (C) smart
   (D) bark   (E) far   (F) NONE

5. Those dark clouds tell us a _____ is coming.
   (A) jar   (B) fork   (C) score
   (D) snore   (E) storm   (F) NONE

6. I _____ my new coat and hat to school.
   (A) wore   (B) horse   (C) born
   (D) north   (E) cork   (F) NONE

7. Sam broke his _____ when he fell off the bike.
   (A) barn   (B) star   (C) arm
   (D) farm   (E) garden   (F) NONE

8. Tell the _____ to cut your hair very short.
   (A) party   (B) part   (C) hard
   (D) barber   (E) mark   (F) NONE

9. Everyone knows my sister Barbara is very _____.
   (A) park   (B) smart   (C) jar
   (D) car   (E) yard   (F) NONE

10. We need one long rope and two _____ ones.
    (A) north   (B) fork   (C) torch
    (D) storm   (E) porch   (F) NONE

The Second L A P
Language Activity Pages

A. Exercising Your Skill

Fold a sheet of paper into six squares. Copy one of the sets of letters below at the top of each square.

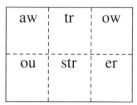

aw	tr	ow
ou	str	er

In each square, write up to seven words that have these letters. Share your lists with two classmates. If you get stuck on some sounds, use a dictionary to find more words.

B. Expanding Your Skill

Fill in these word chains. Write the first and last words on your paper. Leave space between them. Then connect the two words by changing just one letter at a time. The first one is done for you.

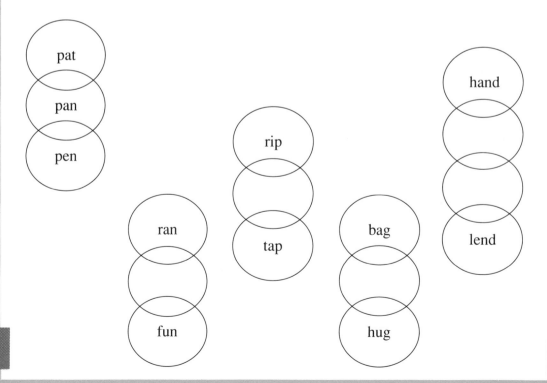

32

C. Exploring Language

Play "Word Chains." Do these steps.

1. Join a team of four to ten students.
2. The first person in each team begins the game by going to the chalkboard and writing a three-letter word.
3. Each person on the team goes to the chalkboard in turn. Each one must change one thing about the word to make a new word.

   You may: add one letter

   drop one letter

   change one letter to another letter
4. Use each word only once. If you get stuck, draw a line, then start a new chain with a new three-letter word.

The team with the longest word chain wins the game.

D. Expressing Yourself

Choose one of these things.

1. Pick one of the word chains from Part B or make up a new chain. Write a story that uses all the words in that chain.

2. Make up a secret code. Write each letter in the alphabet. Write a number under each letter. Write a secret message in code. Use numbers instead of letters. Give the message and the number code to a friend. See if your friend can figure out the message.

1. Mark sewed a button onto his _____.

   (A) never   (B) sir   (C) shirt

   (D) chirp   (E) firm   (F) NONE

2. The _____ took care of the sick child.

   (A) turn   (B) further   (C) fern

   (D) nurse   (E) fir   (F) NONE

3. Mary stepped from the _____ onto the street.

   (A) first   (B) her   (C) churn

   (D) serve   (E) curb   (F) NONE

4. How did you _____ the toast?

   (A) bird   (B) stir   (C) hurt

   (D) curve   (E) burn   (F) NONE

5. How did the _____ get on the rug?

   (A) dirt   (B) jerk   (C) were

   (D) after   (E) whirl   (F) NONE

6. Ron did not want to _____ the eggs.

   (A) purr   (B) fur   (C) surprise

   (D) nervous   (E) servant   (F) NONE

7. Carol is in the _____ grade in school.

   (A) ever   (B) herd   (C) hurt

   (D) thirsty   (E) third   (F) NONE

8. I _____ my knee when I fell off my bike.

   (A) birth   (B) skirt   (C) fire

   (D) thirty   (E) purse   (F) NONE

9. When will dinner be _____?

   (A) curl   (B) turn   (C) baker

   (D) church   (E) burst   (F) NONE

10. Jill's pet bird _____ a merry tune.

    (A) girl   (B) turtle   (C) burn

    (D) service   (E) sir   (F) NONE

1. I will study for the test during the _____.
    - (A) weekend
    - (B) rowboat
    - (C) yourself
    - (D) overflow
    - (E) snowshoe
    - (F) NONE

2. Rosa took her bat to the park to play _____ with her friends.
    - (A) fishhook
    - (B) herself
    - (C) baseball
    - (D) horseback
    - (E) grapefruit
    - (F) NONE

3. There were no trees growing on the _____.
    - (A) forever
    - (B) sunrise
    - (C) mountainside
    - (D) sunset
    - (E) seasick
    - (F) NONE

4. We couldn't see far in front because of the _____.
    - (A) without
    - (B) within
    - (C) snowstorm
    - (D) carefree
    - (E) wherever
    - (F) NONE

5. Hang your _____ in the closet.
    - (A) sunbeam
    - (B) raincoat
    - (C) firewood
    - (D) gatepost
    - (E) stairway
    - (F) NONE

6. The boys were caught in the _____ for an hour.
    - (A) thundershower
    - (B) watchdog
    - (C) telltale
    - (D) Thanksgiving
    - (E) basketball
    - (F) NONE

7. The teacher looked at every child's _____.
    - (A) nobody
    - (B) wintertime
    - (C) backwoods
    - (D) seashore
    - (E) workbook
    - (F) NONE

8. Father put the _____ over the children who were sleeping.
    - (A) skyrocket
    - (B) woodland
    - (C) boxcar
    - (D) themselves
    - (E) highway
    - (F) NONE

9. The children got their mother a _____.
    - (A) overflow
    - (B) busybody
    - (C) whichever
    - (D) outdoor
    - (E) backwoods
    - (F) NONE

10. We found these shells at the _____.
    - (A) wherever
    - (B) seashore
    - (C) teamwork
    - (D) himself
    - (E) sunburn
    - (F) NONE

1. I found this letter in our _____ .
    - (A) airport
    - (B) mailbox
    - (C) fishhook
    - (D) earthworms
    - (E) offshore
    - (F) NONE

2. The tired man sat down in the _____ .
    - (A) candlestick
    - (B) streamline
    - (C) tablespoon
    - (D) armchair
    - (E) doorbell
    - (F) NONE

3. The _____ on Jan's shirt was too big for the button.
    - (A) rowboat
    - (B) football
    - (C) highway
    - (D) jellyfish
    - (E) buttonhole
    - (F) NONE

4. At the _____ they looked for signs to help them.
    - (A) crossroads
    - (B) schoolbook
    - (C) raindrop
    - (D) pocketknife
    - (E) daylight
    - (F) NONE

5. The farmer scared the crows away from the _____ .
    - (A) downtown
    - (B) broomstick
    - (C) handbag
    - (D) cornfield
    - (E) horsefly
    - (F) NONE

6. We could not have seen anything without the _____ .
    - (A) buttermilk
    - (B) candlelight
    - (C) catfish
    - (D) overturn
    - (E) flatboat
    - (F) NONE

7. He used a _____ to clean his teeth.
    - (A) yardstick
    - (B) toothpick
    - (C) bookcase
    - (D) anybody
    - (E) nursemaid
    - (F) NONE

8. What is written in your _____ ?
    - (A) notebook
    - (B) dressmaker
    - (C) oxcart
    - (D) drugstore
    - (E) gunboat
    - (F) NONE

9. We cleaned our _____ before Mother came home.
    - (A) rosebud
    - (B) somehow
    - (C) fireworks
    - (D) elsewhere
    - (E) herself
    - (F) NONE

10. The teacher thought the boy might need _____ .
    - (A) eyeglasses
    - (B) battlefield
    - (C) shoemaker
    - (D) barefoot
    - (E) seaport
    - (F) NONE

1. We turned on the _____ and saw Rosa in the cave.

   (A) classroom   (B) lifeboat   (C) homesick

   (D) scrapbook   (E) flashlight   (F) NONE

2. Sandy followed the _____ in the deep snow.

   (A) pancake   (B) battleship   (C) footprints

   (D) teapot   (E) eyesight   (F) NONE

3. The _____ began to twist and turn through the woods.

   (A) warship   (B) hallway   (C) flagpole

   (D) birthday   (E) shoestring   (F) NONE

4. What would you like for your _____ this year?

   (A) tiptoe   (B) birthday   (C) madman

   (D) housefly   (E) goldfish   (F) NONE

5. The farmer worked hard to clear the _____.

   (A) streetcar   (B) moonlight   (C) eyelid

   (D) football   (E) seaweed   (F) NONE

6. We saw a _____ out on the lake.

   (A) steamroller   (B) daydream   (C) motorboat

   (D) soapsuds   (E) underline   (F) NONE

7. Did you see the tree along the _____?

   (A) eyebrow   (B) grasshopper   (C) newspaper

   (D) roadside   (E) bathroom   (F) NONE

8. In the sky _____ the children could see the stars.

   (A) overhead   (B) teaspoon   (C) cowgirl

   (D) daybreak   (E) firelight   (F) NONE

9. We went to the shopping center to buy _____.

   (A) bedroom   (B) dreamland   (C) shipwreck

   (D) wayside   (E) backbone   (F) NONE

10. I will write on the back of this _____.

    (A) postcard   (B) teamwork   (C) bedclothes

    (D) pocketbook   (E) tablespoon   (F) NONE

1. **Plural** means **more than one**. The plural of car is cars. The plural of cat is cats. The plural of some words is made by adding an _____ .
   (A) r   (B) s   (C) m

2. The plural of branch is branches. The plural of wish is wishes. Some words form their plural by adding _____ .
   (A) f   (B) i   (C) es

3. Before you add an **es,** look at the end of the word. The letters at the end of the _____ tell you whether to add an s or es.
   (A) start   (B) word   (C) friend

4. Before you add an **es** to form the _____ , make sure that the word ends with either an **x, s, sh,** or **ch.**
   (A) plural   (B) tree   (C) sentence

5. You can remember the letters **x, s, sh, ch** because they make the same sound as a _____ that is stopping or starting.
   (A) goat   (B) sailboat   (C) train

6. The plural of fo**x** is foxes. The plural of bo**x** is boxes. Words that end with an _____ form their plural by adding **es.**
   (A) h   (B) m   (C) x

7. The plural of kiss is kisses. The plural of dress is dresses. Words that end with an _____ form their plural by adding an **es.**
   (A) s   (B) d   (C) t

8. The plural of bu**sh** is bushes. Words that end with an _____ form their plural by adding an **es.**
   (A) m   (B) d   (C) sh

9. The plural of in**ch** is inches. The plural of ma**tch** is matches. Words that end with a _____ form their plural by adding an **es.**
   (A) k   (B) ch   (C) n

10. If you see the letters **x, s, sh, ch** at the end of a word, be sure to add the letters _____ to the word to make it plural.
    (A) s   (B) es   (C) b

UNIT 30
Doubling Last Letter Concepts

1. The word **double** means **two**. When we double a letter, we make _____ letters that are exactly alike.
   (A) one   (B) two   (C) none

2. Look at the words **run** and **running**. The _____ is doubled before the ending **ing** is added.
   (A) s   (B) n   (C) x

3. Look at the words **cut** and **cutting**. The **t** is doubled before the ending _____ is added.
   (A) ing   (B) ly   (C) ness

4. Look at the words **rub** and **rubbed**. The _____ is doubled before the ending **ed** is added.
   (A) u   (B) r   (C) b

5. Look at the words **bat** and **batted**. The **t** is doubled before the ending _____ is added.
   (A) ed   (B) ly   (C) y

6. Look at the words **drum** and **drummer**. The _____ is doubled before the ending **er** is added.
   (A) m   (B) s   (C) w

7. Look at the words **big** and **bigger**. The **g** is doubled before the ending _____ is added.
   (A) er   (B) y   (C) ish

8. Look at the words **run, cut, rub, bat, swim, big.** The next to the last letter of each word is a _____.
   (A) vowel   (B) consonant   (C) nothing

9. Look at the words **run, cut, rub, bat, swim, big.** The last letter of each word is a _____.
   (A) candy   (B) consonant   (C) vowel

10. When only one vowel is followed by a consonant, the last consonant is doubled before the _____ **ing, ed, er** are added.
    (A) endings   (B) words   (C) beginnings

1. Look at the last letter in the words **party, baby, puppy.** All of these words
   _____ with a **y.**

   (A) start   (B) end   (C) laugh

2. Look at the words **party** and **parties.** In the word **parties** the **y** was
   changed to an **i** before the ending **es** was _____.

   (A) eaten   (B) dropped   (C) added

3. Look at the words **penny** and **pennies.** The letter **y** was changed to an **i**
   before the ending _____ was added.

   (A) tion   (B) es   (C) xyz

4. Look at the words **easy** and **easier.** In the word **easier** the **y** was changed
   to an _____ before the ending **er** was added.

   (A) i   (B) t   (C) m

5. Look at the words **silly** and **sillier.** In the word **sillier** the **y** was changed to
   an **i** before the ending _____ was added.

   (A) ckt   (B) er   (C) ck

6. Look at the words **funny** and **funniest.** In the word **funniest** the **y** was
   changed to an _____ before the ending **est** was added.

   (A) i   (B) r   (C) fairy

7. Look at the words **pretty** and **prettiest.** In the word **prettiest** the **y** was
   changed to an **i** before the ending _____ was added.

   (A) est   (B) ark   (C) ity

8. Look at the words **merry** and **merrily.** In the word **merrily** the **y** was
   _____ to an **i** before the ending **ly** was added.

   (A) crushed   (B) changed   (C) broken

9. Look at the words **busy** and **busily.** In the word **busily** the **y** was changed
   to an **i** before the ending _____ was added.

   (A) ly   (B) uny   (C) bomb

10. The last _____ often changes to an **i** before endings **es, er, est, ly** are
    added.

    (A) m   (B) s   (C) y

1. Some letters do not make any sounds. These letters are called _____ letters.

   (A) little   (B) silent   (C) loud

2. Look at the word **light**. Say each sound as you look at the letters. There is no sound for letters _____.

   (A) gh   (B) ig   (C) ht

3. What is the silent letter in the word **climb**? The _____ at the end of the word has no sound.

   (A) m   (B) p   (C) b

4. Look at the word **know**. Say each sound as you look at the letters. There is a **k** just before the **n.** We hear the **n** but not the _____.

   (A) i   (B) k   (C) r

5. Say the word **write**. The letter **w** is silent when it comes just before the _____.

   (A) r   (B) i   (C) vowel

6. Many words end with the letter **e**. Look at the word **cake**. In such words the _____ letter is silent.

   (A) first   (B) consonant   (C) last

7. Look at the words **goat** and **rain**. We hear the first vowel but not the _____.

   (A) big   (B) second   (C) s

8. Say the word **match** slowly. You do not hear the _____ when it comes before the **ch**.

   (A) r   (B) t   (C) a

9. Some words end with two letters that are the same. Look at the words **ball** and **miss**. We hear the first of the twin consonants, but not the _____.

   (A) third   (B) last   (C) e

10. Look at the words **kitten** and **little**. There are two **t**'s in each word. The second **t** is _____.

    (A) hurry   (B) sick   (C) silent

1. The bird came to get the _____ of bread.
   - **(A) crumb**
   - **(B) dumb**
   - **(C) climb**
   - **(D) comb**
   - **(E) limb**
   - **(F) NONE**

2. Which _____ turns on the light?
   - **(A) ditch**
   - **(B) witch**
   - **(C) switch**
   - **(D) stretch**
   - **(E) watch**
   - **(F) NONE**

3. Bob hurt his _____ when he fell on a rock.
   - **(A) knob**
   - **(B) knock**
   - **(C) knee**
   - **(D) knit**
   - **(E) kneel**
   - **(F) NONE**

4. You could tell it was _____ by a young child.
   - **(A) wrist**
   - **(B) wren**
   - **(C) wrong**
   - **(D) wrinkle**
   - **(E) written**
   - **(F) NONE**

5. The _____ is very sharp.
   - **(A) knife**
   - **(B) knight**
   - **(C) knelt**
   - **(D) knew**
   - **(E) knot**
   - **(F) NONE**

6. Mother said that she _____ come home early today.
   - **(A) sight**
   - **(B) high**
   - **(C) bright**
   - **(D) right**
   - **(E) light**
   - **(F) NONE**

7. Mark tried to lift the heavy _____.
   - **(A) shine**
   - **(B) hope**
   - **(C) grade**
   - **(D) white**
   - **(E) blame**
   - **(F) NONE**

8. Don't _____ that glass of milk.
   - **(A) class**
   - **(B) miss**
   - **(C) spill**
   - **(D) bluff**
   - **(E) swell**
   - **(F) NONE**

9. Dad said he liked fresh _____ in his coffee.
   - **(A) waist**
   - **(B) paint**
   - **(C) claim**
   - **(D) treat**
   - **(E) float**
   - **(F) NONE**

10. Betty had a new watch around her _____.
    - **(A) wring**
    - **(B) wreck**
    - **(C) wrist**
    - **(D) write**
    - **(E) wrote**
    - **(F) NONE**

UNIT 34
Building Variant Sound Concepts

1. The letter **c** has two sounds. Sometimes it sounds like a **k**. Sometimes it
   _____ like an **s.**
   (A) sounds   (B) looks   (C) runs

2. Say the words **coat, camp, come.** In these words the _____ sounds
   like a **k.**
   (A) m   (B) c   (C) b

3. When the letter **c** sounds like a _____, it is said to have a hard sound.
   (A) k   (B) r   (C) 1

4. Sometimes the letter _____ sounds like an **s.**
   (A) c   (B) r   (C) 1

5. Say the words **city, center, race.** In these words the letter **c** sounds like an
   _____.
   (A) t   (B) s   (C) m

6. When a **c** sounds like an **s,** it is said to have a soft _____.
   (A) landing   (B) pillow   (C) sound

7. The letter **g** has _____ sounds. Sometimes it sounds like **g** in the word **go.**
   Sometimes it sounds like a **j.**
   (A) two   (B) ten   (C) none

8. Say the words **get, gum.** In these words the **g** sounds as it does in the word
   _____. It is said to have a hard sound.
   (A) run   (B) Jane   (C) go

9. Sometimes the _____ sounds like a **j.**
   (A) g   (B) s   (C) c

10. Say the words **page, gym, orange.** In these words the **g** has a _____
    sound. It is said to have a soft sound.
    (A) j   (B) b   (C) t

1. A house is often broken into parts. These parts are called rooms. Some houses have only one room. Other houses have _____ rooms.

    (A) many   **(B) red**   **(C) floor**

2. Some words have parts, just as houses have rooms. These _____ of words are called syllables.

    (A) sentences   **(B) parts**   **(C) numbers**

3. The word **win ter** is broken into syllables. There is a little _____ between the syllables.

    (A) monkey   **(B) friend**   **(C) space**

4. How many syllables are in the word **get?**

    (A) one   **(B) two**   **(C) three**

5. How many syllables are in the word **pic nic?**

    (A) one   **(B) two**   **(C) three**

6. How many syllables are in the word **af ter noon?**

    (A) one   **(B) two**   **(C) three**

7. How many syllables are in the word **tel e vi sion?**

    (A) two   **(B) three**   **(C) four**

8. Words do not always have the same _____ of syllables.

    (A) number   **(B) sentence**   **(C) train**

9. In the word **cat** you hear one vowel sound. There is also just _____ syllable.

    (A) two   **(B) ten**   **(C) one**

10. In the word **rab bit** you hear two vowel sounds, the short **a** and the short **i**. There are also _____ syllables.

    (A) one   **(B) two**   **(C) three**

1. In the word **ac ci dent** you hear three vowel sounds, the short **a**, the short **i**, and the short **e.** There are also _____ syllables.

   (A) one   **(B) four**   **(C) three**

2. In the word **at trac tive ly** you hear four vowel sounds, the short **a,** the short **a,** the short **i,** and the long **e.** There are also _____ syllables.

   (A) two   **(B) four**   **(C) six**

3. We have found that there are the same number of _____ as there are vowel sounds.

   (A) syllables   **(B) boys**   **(C) consonants**

4. Clap your hands as you say each syllable of the word **pic nic.** You clapped _____ times.

   (A) one   **(B) five**   **(C) two**

5. Clap your hands as you say each syllable of the word **re mem ber.** You clapped _____ times.

   (A) six   **(B) nine**   **(C) three**

6. Clap your hands as you say each syllable of the word **un der.** You clapped _____ times.

   (A) two   **(B) three**   **(C) four**

7. Between what two letters is the word **but ton** broken into syllables?

   (A) t and t   **(B) c and t**   **(C) a and b**

8. Between what two letters is the word **num ber** broken into syllables?

   (A) e and r   **(B) u and m**   **(C) m and b**

9. Between what two letters is the word **per son** broken into syllables?

   (A) r and s   **(B) i and c**   **(C) p and i**

10. Between what two letters is the word **sum mer** broken into syllables?

    (A) s and m   **(B) m and m**   **(C) t and x**

1. What is the first vowel in the word **winter?**

   (A) e   (B) i   (C) n

2. In the word **winter** (V) the letter **V** is over the first _____.

   (A) **vowel**   (B) **r**   (C) **t**

3. In the word **winter** (VCC) there is a **C** over each of the two _____ that come right after the first vowel.

   (A) **x's**   (B) **l's**   (C) **consonants**

4. In the word **winter** (VCC) the **n** and **t** are consonants. The **e** that follows those consonants is a _____.

   (A) **vowel**   (B) **x**   (C) **r**

5. In the word **tiger** (VC) the marks above the letters show that there is only _____ consonant right after the first vowel.

   (A) **two**   (B) **one**   (C) **no**

6. In the word **lobster** (VCCC) the marks above the letters show that there are _____ consonants right after the first vowel.

   (A) **three**   (B) **two**   (C) **ten**

7. The marks above the letters in the words **tiger** (VC)**, winter** (VCC)**, lobster** (VCCC) show that the number of _____ after the first vowel is not always the same.

   (A) **boys**   (B) **sentences**   (C) **consonants**

8. Two-syllable words such as **win ter** (VC C) are called **VCC** words because there are two _____ right after the first vowel.

   (A) **dogs**   (B) **consonants**   (C) **vowels**

9. Count the consonants that come right after the first vowel in the word **forget.** There are _____ consonants.

   (A) **two**   (B) **three**   (C) **five**

10. Look at the two consonants after the first vowel in the word **but ter.** These two consonants are called twin consonants because they look _____.

    (A) **fat**   (B) **alike**   (C) **silly**

1. In the word **rab bit** there are _____ consonants right after the first vowel.
   (A) no   (B) six   (C) twin

2. Look at the two consonants that come right after the vowel **u** in the word **number.** These two consonants do not look _____.
   (A) alike   (B) different   (C) neat

3. The word **mem ber** is broken between the two consonants **m** and _____.
   (A) b   (B) e   (C) m

4. The word **sen tence** is broken between the two consonants **n** and _____.
   (A) t   (B) e   (C) x

5. The word **bar ber** is broken _____ the two consonants **r** and **b**.
   (A) after   (B) between   (C) before

6. The word **sum mer** is _____ between the two consonants **m** and **m**.
   (A) vowel   (B) sentence   (C) broken

7. Words that have two consonants right after the first vowel are usually broken between the _____ consonants.
   (A) two   (B) one   (C) four

8. The vowel **u** in the word **but ton** is in the middle of the first syllable. The vowel has a _____ sound.
   (A) long   (B) short   (C) silent

9. In the word **let ter** the first **t** goes with the _____ syllable.
   (A) last   (B) third   (C) first

10. In the word **win ter** the **n** goes with the first syllable. The **t** goes with the second _____.
    (A) syllable   (B) friend   (C) letter

A. Exercising Your Skill

A **compound word** is one word made up of two other words. Make compound-word stairs. On each stair, make a new compound word. Use the last half of the word from the stair above. Use words from the list to help you make new compounds.

Draw the stairs. Write in the compound words. The first one is done for you.

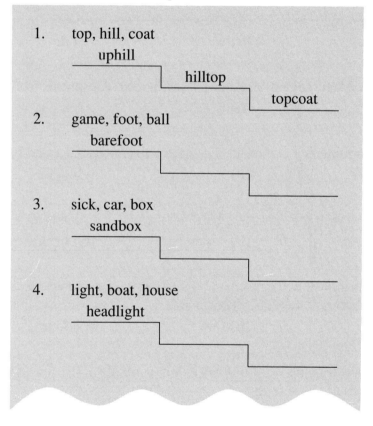

1. top, hill, coat
   uphill
   hilltop
   topcoat

2. game, foot, ball
   barefoot

3. sick, car, box
   sandbox

4. light, boat, house
   headlight

B. Expanding Your Skill

How many word stairs can you make? Brainstorm with a team of classmates. See how many compound-word stairs you can put together.

Need ideas? Some words used in compounds are: board, ball, door, foot, sun, water, book, head, and wind. Think of others on your own.

C. Exploring Language

Finish each sentence below by adding at least one compound word. You may also need to add words such as **a, the**, and **and**. Write the sentences on your paper.

1. My family went to see _____ .
2. While we were there we ate _____ .
3. We saw _____ flying in the sky.
4. We all played _____ at the park.
5. Pat lost _____ in the grass.
6. Alex found _____ on the ground.
7. Then we went shopping at _____ .
8. We didn't go home until after _____ .

D. Expressing Yourself

Choose one of these things.

1. Play a game of "Charades" using compound words. Form two teams. Your teacher will give you the words to act out. Act out one part of the word at a time. Have one student be the timekeeper. See if your team can guess the compound word in three minutes.

2. Play a game of "Hangman." If you do not know how to play, ask your teacher to explain the game. Use only compound words for your partner to guess. If you cannot think of a compound, look in a reading book or dictionary to find one.

3. Cut out twenty strips of paper or cardboard. Write the first half of ten compound words on ten strips. Write the second half of each word on the other ten strips. Let your classmates have fun putting the compound words together.

1. We saw lions and tigers at the _____.
    (A) tunnel   (B) happen   (C) circus
    (D) permit   (E) number   (F) NONE

2. Use a _____ when you sit down to eat dinner.
    (A) perhaps   (B) public   (C) napkin
    (D) fellow   (E) sudden   (F) NONE

3. The children saw the _____ show at school.
    (A) enter   (B) lesson   (C) puppet
    (D) under   (E) button   (F) NONE

4. Rest your head on this _____.
    (A) fifteen   (B) pillow   (C) lantern
    (D) sister   (E) person   (F) NONE

5. Did you _____ the movie last night?
    (A) winter   (B) enjoy   (C) pretty
    (D) gallop   (E) dinner   (F) NONE

6. We could see the lightning and hear the _____.
    (A) muffin   (B) bitten   (C) thunder
    (D) matter   (E) silver   (F) NONE

7. I received a _____ from my Aunt Jean.
    (A) letter   (B) picnic   (C) subject
    (D) plastic   (E) twenty   (F) NONE

8. Rosa is going to learn to play the _____.
    (A) Sunday   (B) lettuce   (C) zipper
    (D) cricket   (E) trumpet   (F) NONE

9. Yesterday Mark read the first _____ of the book.
    (A) signal   (B) bottom   (C) contest
    (D) chapter   (E) pillow   (F) NONE

10. Robert got a bad _____ on his left foot.
    (A) elbow   (B) supper   (C) winner
    (D) yellow   (E) carpet   (F) NONE

1. We plan to have a _____ in the park.
   - (A) elbow
   - (B) indeed
   - (C) helmet
   - (D) matter
   - (E) picnic
   - (F) NONE

2. Mrs. Carter said that Ann's paper was _____ .
   - (A) perfect
   - (B) order
   - (C) trumpet
   - (D) twenty
   - (E) butter
   - (F) NONE

3. Tom's _____ broke while he was writing with it.
   - (A) supper
   - (B) after
   - (C) blossom
   - (D) ladder
   - (E) turkey
   - (F) NONE

4. Pam soon became a _____ of the baseball team.
   - (A) cotton
   - (B) bottom
   - (C) member
   - (D) indeed
   - (E) trombone
   - (F) NONE

5. I didn't see you sitting there in the _____ .
   - (A) corner
   - (B) pencil
   - (C) sadden
   - (D) temper
   - (E) target
   - (F) NONE

6. Father's _____ were too small for his feet.
   - (A) candy
   - (B) slippers
   - (C) whiskers
   - (D) summers
   - (E) until
   - (F) NONE

7. My brother fell and hurt his _____ .
   - (A) traffic
   - (B) doctor
   - (C) elbow
   - (D) wonderful
   - (E) winner
   - (F) NONE

8. Mother bought some _____ to build the bookcase.
   - (A) hidden
   - (B) lumber
   - (C) dollar
   - (D) pillow
   - (E) swimmer
   - (F) NONE

9. Our feet were too muddy to walk on the _____ .
   - (A) thirty
   - (B) jelly
   - (C) carpet
   - (D) invite
   - (E) rubber
   - (F) NONE

10. We have _____ of food for everyone.
    - (A) tennis
    - (B) flower
    - (C) plenty
    - (D) walrus
    - (E) mitten
    - (F) NONE

1. What is the first vowel in the word **decide?**

   (A) **i**   (B) **e**   (C) **u**

2. In the word $\overset{v}{\text{decide}}$ there is a V over the first _____.

   (A) **x**   (B) **consonant**   (C) **vowel**

3. In the word $\overset{vc}{\text{decide}}$ the marks above the letters show that there is only one _____ after the first vowel.

   (A) **girl**   (B) **consonant**   (C) **word**

4. In the word $\overset{vc}{\text{hotel}}$ the marks above the letters show that there is only one consonant right after the first vowel. The next letter **e** is not a _____.

   (A) **letter**   (B) **vowel**   (C) **consonant**

5. Two-syllable words such as $\overset{vc}{\text{tiger}}$ are called **VC** words since there is only one consonant after the first _____.

   (A) **vowel**   (B) **friend**   (C) **week**

6. Find the vowel **i** in the word **ti ger.** The vowel **i** comes at the _____ of the first syllable.

   (A) **middle**   (B) **end**   (C) **start**

7. Find the first vowel in the word **ho tel.** The vowel **o** comes at the end of the _____ syllable.

   (A) **second**   (B) **third**   (C) **first**

8. Find the first vowel in the word **mu sic.** The vowel **u** comes at the end of the first _____.

   (A) **night**   (B) **day**   (C) **syllable**

9. In most VC words the first vowel comes at the _____ of the first syllable.

   (A) **end**   (B) **start**   (C) **most**

10. Look at the consonant **t** in the word **ho tel.** The consonant **t** is part of the second _____.

    (A) **letter**   (B) **syllable**   (C) **week**

UNIT 42
Building VC Pattern Concepts

1. Look at the consonant **t** in the word **mo tor.** The consonant **t** is part of the _____ syllable.
   (A) **first**   (B) **second**   (C) **third**

2. Say the first syllable in the word **ti ger.** The **i** at the end of the first syllable has a long **i** _____.
   (A) **sound**   (B) **silent**   (C) **consonant**

3. Say the first syllable of the word **ho tel.** The **o** at the end of the first syllable has a _____ o sound.
   (A) **short**   (B) **long**   (C) **silent**

4. Say the first syllable of the word **mu sic.** The **u** at the end of the first syllable has a long _____ sound.
   (A) **u**   (B) **a**   (C) **foolish**

5. A vowel that comes at the end of the first syllable usually has a _____ sound.
   (A) **silly**   (B) **long**   (C) **silent**

6. In most VC words the vowel comes at the end of the first _____, but in some words this does not happen.
   (A) **syllable**   (B) **day**   (C) **letter**

7. Look at the word **nev er.** In this word the first syllable ends with a _____, as the marks above the letters show.
   (A) **consonant**   (B) **sentence**   (C) **vowel**

8. The first vowel in the word **nev er** is in the middle of the first syllable. This vowel **e** has a _____ sound.
   (A) **silent**   (B) **short**   (C) **long**

9. In most words such as **clo ver, ho tel, ti ny, ti ger,** the vowel comes at the end of the first syllable and it is _____.
   (A) **long**   (B) **absent**   (C) **short**

10. When you see a VC word, first try a long vowel sound. If the word doesn't sound right, then try a short vowel _____.
    (A) **sound**   (B) **x**   (C) **silent**

1. Bring your radio and we can listen to _____.

    (A) lazy   (B) fever   (C) music

    (D) hotel   (E) bacon   (F) NONE

2. Tom saw a _____ climbing up the wall.

    (A) flavor   (B) spider   (C) over

    (D) position   (E) total   (F) NONE

3. A _____ is a very pretty flower.

    (A) paper   (B) tulip   (C) crazy

    (D) polite   (E) pupil   (F) NONE

4. Will you help me _____ this can?

    (A) November   (B) tiger   (C) navy

    (D) silent   (E) open   (F) NONE

5. They lived in a very warm _____.

    (A) famous   (B) notify   (C) select

    (D) climate   (E) zero   (F) NONE

6. Would you like a _____ with your steak?

    (A) frozen   (B) potato   (C) final

    (D) silence   (E) Venus   (F) NONE

7. Juan walked to the railroad _____ to meet Bob.

    (A) station   (B) locate   (C) minus

    (D) season   (E) tiny   (F) NONE

8. May we sit on the _____?

    (A) lady   (B) clover   (C) hobo

    (D) stolen   (E) sofa   (F) NONE

9. My family will go on a trip in _____.

    (A) beaver   (B) July   (C) idea

    (D) solo   (E) Sunday   (F) NONE

10. Would Karen do a _____ for me?

    (A) locust   (B) favor   (C) gravy

    (D) tuna   (E) cider   (F) NONE

1. Look at the words **table, apple, sparkle.** The last two letters in each word are _____.

    (A) alike·   (B) different   (C) cw

2. Such words as **table, apple, sparkle** are called **"le"** words because they end with an _____.

    (A) el   (B) le   (C) rt

3. Count the letters in the last syllable of the word **spar kle.** There are _____.

    (A) one   (B) two   (C) three

4. Look at the last syllable of the word **ta ble.** The last syllable begins with a _____.

    (A) b   (B) 1   (C) n

5. Look at the last syllable of the words **ap ple, spar kle, ta ble.** The "le" always has another _____ with it.

    (A) number   (B) letter   (C) elephant

6. Look at the word **ta ble.** It is broken before the _____.

    (A) r   (B) n   (C) last three letters

7. Say the last syllable of the word **ta ble.** The **le** sounds like _____.

    (A) r   (B) "ull" as in the   (C) g
                           word *full*

8. Say the last syllable of the word **spar kle.** The **e** at the end is silent. It is not _____.

    (A) heard   (B) pretty   (C) anything

9. Look at the twin consonants before **le** in the word **ket tle.** The two consonants look _____.

    (A) alike   (B) different   (C) funny

10. Say the word **ket tle.** The two consonant **t's** are alike. We hear the first **t.** The second _____ is silent.

    (A) b   (B) d   (C) t

1. I put one _____ on the birthday cake.
   - (A) juggle
   - (B) table
   - (C) bubble
   - (D) simple
   - (E) candle
   - (F) NONE

2. The _____ on my lunch box is broken.
   - (A) sample
   - (B) handle
   - (C) riddle
   - (D) jungle
   - (E) table
   - (F) NONE

3. Maria went into the _____ to see her pony.
   - (A) buckle
   - (B) tickle
   - (C) battle
   - (D) stable
   - (E) bugle
   - (F) NONE

4. We saw a herd of _____ on the ranch.
   - (A) pebble
   - (B) eagle
   - (C) cradle
   - (D) cattle
   - (E) thimble
   - (F) NONE

5. How did you _____ on the stairs?
   - (A) stumble
   - (B) rattle
   - (C) able
   - (D) marble
   - (E) apple
   - (F) NONE

6. A _____ can pull its head inside its shell.
   - (A) poodle
   - (B) gobble
   - (C) turtle
   - (D) gentle
   - (E) middle
   - (F) NONE

7. John could not fit all the pieces in his _____.
   - (A) needle
   - (B) grumble
   - (C) puzzle
   - (D) maple
   - (E) purple
   - (F) NONE

8. Sam was able to open the _____ of milk.
   - (A) nibble
   - (B) castle
   - (C) bottle
   - (D) rifle
   - (E) giggle
   - (F) NONE

9. Some people do not use a _____ when riding a horse.
   - (A) kettle
   - (B) maple
   - (C) saddle
   - (D) beetle
   - (E) title
   - (F) NONE

10. They were not _____ to answer the question.
    - (A) gargle
    - (B) tumble
    - (C) apple
    - (D) able
    - (E) paddle
    - (F) NONE

1. Do you _____ how to do this math problem?
   - **(A) subject**
   - **(B) understand**
   - **(C) remain**
   - **(D) program**
   - **(E) hospital**
   - **(F) NONE**

2. We watched all the _____ get off the ship.
   - **(A) napkins**
   - **(B) pavement**
   - **(C) passengers**
   - **(D) announce**
   - **(E) information**
   - **(F) NONE**

3. This road is very _____ when it is wet.
   - **(A) garbage**
   - **(B) possibly**
   - **(C) slippery**
   - **(D) position**
   - **(E) potatoes**
   - **(F) NONE**

4. Andy said he had some _____ news to tell Pat.
   - **(A) influence**
   - **(B) position**
   - **(C) deliver**
   - **(D) important**
   - **(E) border**
   - **(F) NONE**

5. Dan's mother worked in an airplane _____.
   - **(A) memory**
   - **(B) family**
   - **(C) magnet**
   - **(D) direction**
   - **(E) factory**
   - **(F) NONE**

6. Jill put the _____ into the mailbox on the corner.
   - **(A) envelope**
   - **(B) entire**
   - **(C) tomorrow**
   - **(D) admit**
   - **(E) introduce**
   - **(F) NONE**

7. Please do not write _____ this line.
   - **(A) appoint**
   - **(B) return**
   - **(C) below**
   - **(D) defend**
   - **(E) recent**
   - **(F) NONE**

8. Rosa was _____ to be the club's president.
   - **(A) student**
   - **(B) chosen**
   - **(C) banner**
   - **(D) defeat**
   - **(E) spoken**
   - **(F) NONE**

9. Tom tried to _____ how to spell every word.
   - **(A) recover**
   - **(B) distant**
   - **(C) remember**
   - **(D) mental**
   - **(E) ability**
   - **(F) NONE**

10. Did you see the _____ at the zoo?
    - **(A) elephant**
    - **(B) address**
    - **(C) hundred**
    - **(D) around**
    - **(E) anxious**
    - **(F) NONE**

1. What is causing all the _____ on this highway?
   - (A) raccoon
   - (B) stretch
   - (C) perhaps
   - (D) attention
   - (E) traffic
   - (F) NONE

2. Peter added a new stamp to his _____.
   - (A) yesterday
   - (B) invention
   - (C) collection
   - (D) marvelous
   - (E) improvement
   - (F) NONE

3. I thought the show we saw was _____.
   - (A) rescue
   - (B) remove
   - (C) wonderful
   - (D) bicycle
   - (E) increase
   - (F) NONE

4. We rode on an _____ to get to the tenth floor.
   - (A) inspect
   - (B) president
   - (C) pretend
   - (D) introduce
   - (E) elevator
   - (F) NONE

5. Ron asked his mother for a cool glass of _____.
   - (A) lemonade
   - (B) valentine
   - (C) moment
   - (D) company
   - (E) statement
   - (F) NONE

6. It was _____ to light the fire because of the rain.
   - (A) darkness
   - (B) prevent
   - (C) subtraction
   - (D) interest
   - (E) difficult
   - (F) NONE

7. Sandy said she was going to go away on her _____.
   - (A) package
   - (B) spoken
   - (C) vacation
   - (D) concrete
   - (E) approve
   - (F) NONE

8. Maria said she read an _____ book over the weekend.
   - (A) interesting
   - (B) surround
   - (C) opposite
   - (D) empty
   - (E) attention
   - (F) NONE

9. Father sent Andy to the _____ to get some cake.
   - (A) remember
   - (B) bakery
   - (C) silence
   - (D) following
   - (E) nervous
   - (F) NONE

10. We waited on the _____ for the train to arrive.
    - (A) powder
    - (B) possibly
    - (C) repair
    - (D) different
    - (E) depend
    - (F) NONE

1. A root is the main part of a word. It is the _____ to which other parts can be added.

   (A) laugh   **(B) part**   **(C) letter**

2. In the word **sings** the letter **s** was added to the _____ word **sing.**

   (A) root   **(B) fun**   **(C) tree**

3. The root of the word **plays** is **play.** The root of the word **unfair** is **fair.** The root of the word **walking** is _____.

   (A) walk   **(B) walki**   **(C) walkin**

4. Look at the words **untrue, unhappy, unlock.** Each of these words has a part added in front of the _____.

   (A) I   **(B) m**   **(C) root**

5. The part added in front of the root is called a **prefix.** In the word **unlock** the _____ is **un.**

   (A) prefix   **(B) root**   **(C) sad**

6. The prefix **un** often means the same as **not.** Unhappy means not happy. Untold means not told. Unripe means _____ ripe.

   (A) sweet   **(B) not**   **(C) mostly**

7. The prefix **un** sometimes means **the opposite of.** Unpack means the opposite of pack. Unlock means the _____ of lock.

   (A) opposite   **(B) same**   **(C) little**

8. Look at the words **reread, rewrite, refill, rebuild.** The prefix in all of these words is _____.

   (A) missing   **(B) re**   **(C) un**

9. The prefix **re** means **again.** To reread means to read again. To rewrite means to write _____.

   (A) again   **(B) letters**   **(C) wrong**

10. Look at the words **unafraid, repay, broke, rebuild.** The word _____ is the only one without a prefix.

    (A) repay   **(B) unafraid**   **(C) broke**

1. A suffix is a word part _____ to the end of a root word.
    (A) buttoned   **(B) added**   **(C) hammer**

2. Some of the word endings or _____ are **less, ful, er, est, ish, y, ness.**
    (A) suffixes   **(B) sentences**   **(C) houses**

3. Cloud**less** means without clouds. Care**less** means without care. A **less** at the end of a word means _____.
    (A) without   **(B) with**   **(C) more**

4. Care**ful** means full of care. Mouth**ful** means a mouth that is full. A **ful** at the end of a word means to be _____ with.
    (A) not   **(B) filled**   **(C) without**

5. A work**er** is a person who works. A swimm**er** is one who swims. An **er** at the end of a word means _____ who is or does something.
    (A) elephant   **(B) little**   **(C) one**

6. Green**ish** means somewhat green. Yellow**ish** means somewhat yellow. Clown**ish** means _____ like a clown.
    (A) boy   **(B) somewhat**   **(C) nothing**

7. Ill**ness** means being ill. Happi**ness** means being happy. Silli**ness** means _____ silly.
    (A) being   **(B) not**   **(C) went**

8. Slow**ly** means in a slow way. Quick**ly** means in a quick manner or way. Soft**ly** means in a soft _____.
    (A) rock   **(B) hill**   **(C) way**

9. Rock**y** means having rocks. Bump**y** means full of bumps or having bumps. Luck**y** means _____ luck.
    (A) having   **(B) without**   **(C) bad**

10. Fast**est** means that no one is as fast. Small**est** means that no one is as small. The **est** at the end of the word makes the word mean _____ than anybody or anything else.
    (A) same   **(B) more**   **(C) less**

1. The play _____ kittens are fun to watch.

   (A) ish   (B) ful   (C) er

   (D) est   (E) ly   (F) NONE

2. I believe the car was a brown _____ color.

   (A) y   (B) ness   (C) ish

   (D) ful   (E) ly   (F) NONE

3. He must wash all those dirt _____ socks.

   (A) est   (B) er   (C) ly

   (D) y   (E) less   (F) NONE

4. It was the dark _____ sky I had ever seen.

   (A) ful   (B) ish   (C) ly

   (D) less   (E) est   (F) NONE

5. Meg can run fast _____ than Barbara or Bill.

   (A) ly   (B) ful   (C) y

   (D) less   (E) er   (F) NONE

6. The nurse told me the name of the sick _____.

   (A) ish   (B) ful   (C) less

   (D) ness   (E) y   (F) NONE

7. The little dog was home _____.

   (A) ish   (B) less   (C) er

   (D) est   (E) ful   (F) NONE

8. We all walked quick _____ to the classroom.

   (A) ful   (B) y   (C) ly

   (D) ness   (E) ish   (F) NONE

9. Ben was fool _____ to leave his bike there.

   (A) ful   (B) er   (C) ness

   (D) ly   (E) less   (F) NONE

10. Sam was the kind _____ person I ever met.

    (A) ful   (B) y   (C) est

    (D) ness   (E) ly   (F) NONE

A. Exercising Your Skill

A **prefix** is a word part that is added at the beginning of a word. A **suffix** is a word part that is added at the end of a word. Look at the words in the box. Can you find the prefix or suffix in each of these words?

replay	unhappy	playful	hopeless

Here are the meanings of the prefixes and suffixes in the words above.

Prefix	Meaning	Suffix	Meaning
re	again	ful	filled with
un	not; opposite of	less	without

When a prefix or suffix is added to a word, it changes the meaning of the word. For example, the word **redo** means **do again**.

Write the words **replay, unhappy, playful,** and **hopeless** on your paper. Next to each word write its meaning.

B. Expanding Your Skill

Add a prefix or suffix to each word below. Write the new word and its meaning on your paper.

finished	cooked	pain
lock	joy	care

Get together with others in your class to share words. How many different words can you make by adding prefixes and suffixes to the words above? Add as many new words as you can think of to the ones you have already written on your paper.

C. Exploring Language

1. Write a sentence that includes a word with the prefix **re**.
2. Write a sentence that includes a word with the prefix **un**.
3. Write a sentence that includes a word with the suffix **ful**.
4. Write a sentence that includes a word with the suffix **less**.

D. Expressing Yourself

Choose one of these things.

1. Write a funny story about two children trying to cook a meal. In your story use as many words with prefixes and suffixes as you can.

2. Make as many new words as you can by adding prefixes and suffixes to the word **use**. Use each new word you make in a sentence.

3. What is the difference between a bed that is **made** and a bed that is **unmade**? The words **made** and **unmade** are opposites. The words **hopeful** and **hopeless** are opposites, too. How many opposites can you make by adding prefixes or suffixes to words? Write as many opposite word pairs as you can think of. This is a good activity to do with a partner or in a group. You will think of more word pairs when you are working together.

CONCEPTS DEVELOPED